ABC

for
JBY

First published in Great Britain by Jonathan Cape Ltd in 1989
First published in Picture Lions in 1990
This edition published in 1992
Picture Lions is an imprint of the Children's Division,
part of HarperCollins Publishers Limited,
77-85 Fulham Palace Road, Hammersmith,
London W6 8JB

Printed in Great Britain

Quentin Blake's
ABC

COLLINS
PICTURE LIONS

A B C D
E F G H
I J K L
M N O P
Q R S T
U V W X
Y Z

Aa

A is for Apples,
some green and some red

Bb

B is for Breakfast
we're having in bed

Cc

C is for Cockatoos
learning to scream

Dd

D is for Ducks
upside down in a stream

Ee

E is for Egg
in a nest in a bush

Ff

F is for Firework –
it goes BANG and WHOOSH

Gg

G is for Grandma –
she's really quite fat

H h

H is for Hair
that goes under your hat

Ii

I is for Illness
(which *nobody* likes)

Jj

J is for Junk –
rusty beds and old bikes

K k

K is for Kittens,
all scratching the chair

L l

L is for Legs
that we wave in the air

Mm

M is for Mud
that we get on our knees

Nn

N is for Nose –
and he's going to sneeze!

Oo

O is for Ostrich
who gives us a ride

Pp

P is for Parcel –
let's guess what's inside

Qq

Q is for Queen
with a cloak and a crown

Rr

R is for Roller skates –
watch us fall down!

Ss

S is for Sisters,
some short and some tall

Tt

T is for Tent
where there's room for us all

Uu

U is Umbrella
to keep off the rain

Vv

V is for Vet,
    when your pet has a pain

Ww

W is for Watch –
we can hear the ticktocks

X x

X is the ending
for jack-in-the-boX

Yy

Y is for Yak –
he's our hairiest friend

Zz

Z is for Zippers
That's all
That's the end